Frederic & Elfrida

by JANE AUSTEN

Edited by Peter Sabor, Sylvia Hunt, and Victoria Kortes-Papp

with illustrations by Juliet McMaster

Juvenilia PRESS

Edmonton, Canada, 2002

Frederic & Elfrida
ISBN: 0-9688283-6-1

Contents of the present edition, including text,
editorial matter, notes and illustrations,
Copyright © 2002 Juliet McMaster
General Editor, Juvenilia Press
Department of English
University of Alberta
Edmonton, Alberta, Canada T6G 2E5

Cover and interior illustrations: Juliet McMaster
Cover and interior design: Winston Pei / Black Riders Design

Contents

Acknowledgements
vi

Preface by Victoria Kortes-Papp
vii

Introduction by Sylvia Hunt
ix

Note on the Text by Peter Sabor
xvii

Frederic & Elfrida

by JANE AUSTEN
1

Explanatory Notes by Peter Sabor
20

Illustrator's Note by Juliet McMaster
25

Works Cited
27

Acknowledgements

We are grateful to the Bodleian Library for permitting Peter Sabor to consult the manuscript of *Frederic & Elfrida* in Austen's *Volume the First* (MS. Don. e. 7) and to use it as the basis for this edition. B.C. Barker-Benfield, Geoff Groom, Martin Kauffmann and Steven Tomlinson provided helpful assistance at the Bodleian, and arranged for Peter Sabor to read R.W. Chapman's unpublished correspondence there. Juliet McMaster invited us to undertake this project, furnished us with a microfilm of the manuscript, and gave us valuable advice on all aspects of the edition. We are also indebted to Thomas Keymer, Deirdre Le Faye, and Kathryn Sutherland. Financial support was provided by the Social Sciences and Humanities Research Association of Canada. Rodney Clark, James Hunt, Marie Legroulx, and Michel Morissette provided support of a different kind. Peter Sabor is indebted to Laval University for providing him with a sabbatical leave to work on Austen's juvenilia, and to the Master and Fellows of Christ's College, Cambridge, for awarding him a Bye-Fellowship which enabled him to carry out research in England.

Preface

Frederic & Elfrida is one of Jane Austen's earliest pieces of fiction writing. It is the very first transcribed in her care fully assembled *Volume the First.* Yet it is a piece that has always remained neglected by critics. Her later juvenilia have traditionally garnered more interest, and even among Austen's earliest writings, it has yet to capture its fair share of the spotlight. In this first separate edition of the work, with no weightier successors to vie for our attention, we have the opportunity to consider it more fully, in its significance and its aesthetic.

This piece is no diamond in the rough. It is not, nor does it strive to be, conventionally beautiful, neither does it conceal its beauty subtly beneath its surface. Yet as we make our way through it, what a jewel it is nonetheless: from its first lines to its last it is an intrepid, unashamed, and purposeful satire—characteristics that leave us to imagine what might already have dwelt in the young author.

This miniature story weighs in at just over two thousand three hundred words. Despite their timid number, these words vividly depict characters whose personalities and actions are masterfully wrought to epitomise all that is absurd in novelistic conventions. In its few lines, the story covers the vital subjects of destiny, love, pairings, friendship, marriage, death, correspondence, visiting, names (starting with the very title of the work), settings, timing, conveyances, manners, good taste, sentiment, beauty, vanity, fashion, age. Each subject is taken and reduced to its most trivial essence, in the just service of a good family laugh.

According to the best evidence Austen wrote *Frederic & Elfrida* when she was eleven or twelve years old. We are left to ponder how many novels she would have needed to have read already, and with what close attention, at that very young age to be able to communicate all she does, as she does, with confidence and ease. But even as *Frederic & Elfrida* offers us a humorous crash course in conventional novel patterns, it gives lovers of Austen something much greater. We see in it the author's purposeful carving away of the novelist she will not be, and her early shaping of the novelist she will become.

Uim Korkis-Pargo

Introduction

The Uncle of Elfrida was the Father of Frederic;
in other words, they were first cousins by the Father's side.

This sentence outlining a family connection not only begins the tale of *Frederic & Elfrida* but also marks the start of Jane Austen's foray into authorship at the early age of twelve. Right from this auspicious beginning, Austen's famous wit and intelligence are obvious. For example, the apparently simple sentence that opens this tale is, on initial reading, a standard introduction to the title's characters. Its simplicity, however, is misleading and the relationship requires some deciphering by both the reader and the author to be comprehensible. As David Nokes writes, "Jane Austen has created a nonsensical family riddle in which the roles of uncle, mother and father were all strangely jumbled" (117). A reader unfamiliar with Austen's style may wonder if this convolution is the fault of an inexperienced author or if it is a deliberate, whimsical act. Readers familiar with other Austen works know that the second scenario is the correct one. Although she later suggested that her own writing could be too "light & bright & sparkling" (*Letters*, 203), her juvenilia are full of light and sparkling wit. It is, however, a wit that is regulated by reason. Throughout her juvenilia and later novels, Austen encourages the reader to pause and digest certain passages and decipher the truth that lies beneath.[1] This practice finds its beginnings with the opening line of *Frederic & Elfrida*.

---

1   One of her most famous passages that demands such consideration is another opening sentence, namely that of *Pride and Prejudice.* "It is a truth universally acknowledged, that a single man in possession of a good fortune, must be in want of a wife."

Austen decided at a young age that reading was not a mindless pastime but one that demanded critical thought. A voracious reader herself, she read judiciously, appreciating well-written books. Even less well-constructed novels were considered redeemable since "Nature & Spirit cover many sins of a wandering story" (*Letters*, 269). What she found inexcusable were poorly written novels that offered little to the reader except recycled sentimentalism. Austen's juvenilia represent not only the apprentice work of a budding writer but also a commentary through parody on the ridiculous aspects of the sentimental novel. This sort of parody can be seen throughout the juvenilia. Austen did not live "only through books" (Litz, 5) and develop her artistic style simply by satirizing the conventions of eighteenth-century novels. She was a keen observer of life and manners, and these also provide fodder for her creative talents.

In *Frederic & Elfrida*, she gives the standard sentimental plot of friendships at first sight, protracted engagements and romantic settings a special twist. The melodramatic succession of calamities is conventional, but the mishaps themselves are bizarre and the tone outrageously cavalier. By her offhand tone, Austen downplays the sensational elements of romantic fiction. Her story is highly improbable and morally outrageous, and most of the characters are little more than caricatures, lacking depth and substance.

In order to understand and appreciate Austen's burlesque of the sentimental novel, it is helpful to understand some of the common conventions of the form. B.C. Southam provides a practical list of common characteristics found in most novels of the period (*Literary Manuscripts*, 10-11). One prerequisite is the perfection of the heroine. Not only must she be a physical embodiment of perfection but she must also be pure in nature. A further requirement in the set of characteristics is the trembling sensibility of the hero and heroine, which inevitably leads to love at first sight and instant declarations of love or friendship. This excessive sensibility is ultimately responsible for repeated swooning on the part of the sensitive heroine. In a novel of sensibility a heroine must live constantly in the midst of misfortunes and adventures. She must be virtuous and young, since adventure and sensibility are proper, indeed possible, only to youth. Since sensibility is infinitely varied and beautiful, the language will be full of circumlocution and ornament.

Frederic & Elfrida shows many of the conventions of the standard sentimental novel. For example, most novels of the period include a florid dedication to a patron, which added dignity to the piece. Austen dedicated *Frederic & Elfrida* not to an aristocratic patron, but to a personal friend, Martha Lloyd, whose family had recently come to live at Deane parsonage after the death of Mr. Lloyd. Austen's father had two livings, one at Steventon, where the Austen family lived, and the other at Deane, about one mile away. It was written to thank Martha for her generosity in finishing a "muslin Cloak" for the author. In the story, Austen's heroine greets a new neighbour with praise for her understanding of "the different excellencies of Indian & English Muslins." But if Jane meant this as a compliment to Martha, she negated the effect by Elfrida's savage comments on the "horror" of her new friend's appearance, specifically her "forbidding Squint,...greasy tresses & swelling Back." Poor Martha, as well as her sister Mary, had recently suffered a severe bout of smallpox, which left them both scarred for life. Austen's youthful tactlessness was evident later when she dedicated *Evelyn* to Mary Lloyd. David Nokes writes that "it might perhaps have appeared less than tactful to give Mary a story about a miraculously donated house just at a time when her family was being politely ejected from Deane parsonage" (129).[2]

Central to the plot of a sentimental novel are the many trials

---

2   Later, Mary Lloyd may have found some consolation in a dedicational predicament in which Austen found herself. As a mature author, she attracted the attention of the Prince of Wales, who admired her novels. The Rev. James Stanier Clarke, librarian of the Prince, wrote a letter to the author mentioning that His Royal Highness would be pleased to have her next novel dedicated to him. Despite the fact that Austen disliked the Prince Regent, this was viewed as a command, not a request. As a result, Austen was compelled to dedicate *Emma* to the future king.

imposed on the distressed heroine. For example, Richardson's Clarissa Harlowe is pressured by her family to enter into marriage with a repulsive suitor. These tactics make her vulnerable to Lovelace's advances and ultimately lead to her abduction and rape. In Austen's burlesque of the genre, Charlotte's arrival in London is made dramatic by the ignorance of the postilion, "whose stupidity was amazing" as to their destination. This supposed dilemma is easily resolved when Charlotte, "with the greatest Condescension and Good humour informed him that he was to drive to Portland Place." Being lost and abandoned in the wicked city is a standard situation in novels. Clarissa Harlowe is lured to London, where she has no protection, and is isolated in a brothel by Lovelace. John Cleland's erotic *Memoirs of a Woman of Pleasure* (1748-1749) begins with Fanny Hill descending from a coach alone and unprotected in the vast and unknown city. In Austen's tale, Charlotte is confronted within minutes of her arrival in London with two marriage proposals from two unknown men. The first is a decrepit, elderly gentleman "with a sallow face & old pink Coat." The reader is left to wonder if this suitor is too poor to refurbish his wardrobe and the jacket is a relic of his youth or if he actually continues to think of himself as a young spark. The second suitor is a far more handsome and youthful fellow in a new blue coat, and far more appealing as a marriage prospect. Because of the "natural turn of her mind to make every one happy," Charlotte's initial reaction to this startling event is blind acceptance to both proposals followed by a brief bout of amnesia: "it was not till the next morning that Charlotte recollected the double engagement she had entered into." Overcome with guilt, she throws herself into a stream, drowns, and is miraculously carried to Crankhumdumberry. The object of Austen's satire is silly girls who cannot seem to remember what they said from one minute to another and silly novels that would have us believe that extravagantly ingenuous heroines manage to entangle themselves in innumerable romantic webs.

Austen playfully sends up the sentimental novelists' visible manipulation of time, as in Richardson's epistolary novel *Pamela*

(1740), where the heroine is frantically recording events even while they are happening. Austen uses similar distortions of time for comic effect in her early stories. As Brigid Brophy writes, "the juvenile 'Frederic & Elfrida' whirls ludicrously through time" (36), with important events like Charlotte's suicide and the passage of her body home to Crankhumdunberry being passed over in a sentence. Eighteen years between the marriage of Rebecca and the re-acquaintance of the friends pass by in little more than a single phrase. Meanwhile, a walk in the garden can last for nine hours, and dramatic emphasis is placed on such minor events as the purchase of a bonnet.

A tendency of sentimental and Gothic novel writers was to use exotic locations for the setting of their plots. Rousseau's popular novel *Julie, ou La Nouvelle Héloïse* (1761), for example, is set in the remote Alps, while the original Gothic novel, Horace Walpole's *The Castle of Otranto* (1765), is located in a region of northern Italy. Austen's story is partially set in the less exotic landscape of England, but her simple village with the ridiculous name of Crankhumdunberry is given a description that defies most English landscapes: "...a Grove of Poplars which led from the Parsonage to a verdant Lawn enameled with a variety of variegated flowers & watered by a purling Stream brought from the Valley of Tempé by a passage under ground." Its purling steam is said to find its source in Greece, a geological impossibility. Combined with the distortion of time and the vague family tree, this landscape, a composite of an Irish name, an English landscape and a Greek stream, has an air of fantasy. In *Frederic & Elfrida*, the author has created her own Utopia, but, unlike that conception of perfection, Austen's world is open to ridicule for its improbability.

In many novels, the sensibility of the heroine is physically manifested by her propensity to swoon when overcome by emotion. For example, in Richardson's *Sir Charles Grandison* (1753-1754), one of Austen's favourite novels, the virtuous heroine, Harriet Byron, has a tendency to keel over in fits of unconsciousness. In *Frederic & Elfrida*, Austen ridicules Harriet's frequent fainting by describing a heroine who "was in such a hurry to have a succession of fainting fits, that she had scarcely patience enough to recover from one before she fell into another." Her fragility is amazing for a woman who did not scruple to resolve disagreements with a toss over the windowsill. This delicacy is significantly absent in Austen's later novels, where heroines face adversity upright and conscious.

The convention of using interpolated poems and songs in novels also receives some commentary in *Frederic & Elfrida*. In Sarah Fielding's *The Adventures of David Simple* (1744), for example, each major plot is mirrored in interpolated stories that appear throughout the novel. In Austen's tale, she includes the 'ditty' sung by the Fitzroy sisters about unrequited love, a situation which foreshadows the romantic dilemma an aging Elfrida will face at the end of the tale. Rebecca also sings a simple verse for the entertainment of her friends about the purchase of ribbon at a fair by a beau for his beloved. Despite the references to names found in pastoral poetry, specifically "Damon" in the first song and "Corydon" in the second, the rhymes are forced and the content nonsensical. The epitaph on Charlotte's headstone is not a sentimental elegy commemorating the life of a dear friend but a comical, tasteless bit of verse that summarizes her two great errors in judgment:

> Here lies our friend who having promis-ed
> That unto two she would be marri-ed
> Threw her sweet Body & her lovely face
> Into the Stream that runs thro' Portland Place.

Novels of sensibility used highly ornate language. Sarah Fielding's *The Adventures of David Simple* exemplifies this linguistic ornamentation: " ...the Water, 'ever Friend to Thought,' with the Dashing of the Oars, and the quick Change of Prospect, from where the Houses, at a little distance, seem, by their Number and Thickness, to be built on each other, to the Fields and rural Scenes, naturally threw them into a Humour to reflect on their past Lives" (195). *Frederic & Elfrida* reflects the splendid diction of the sentimental novel in its description of desperate love: "' When the sweet Captain Roger first addressed the amiable Rebecca, you alone objected to their union on account of the tender years of the Parties. That plea can be no more, seven days being now expired, together with the lovely Charlotte, since the Captain first spoke to you on the subject.'"

Besides the parody, *Frederic and Elfrida* contains some biographical elements. To begin with, there is some similarity between the village of Steventon, where her father was rector, described as "one of the prettiest spots" (Austen-Leigh, 14), and "Crankhumdunberry (of which sweet village her [Charlotte's] father was Rector)."

If the fathers of fact and fiction were similar, what of the daughters, Jane and Charlotte? Although Charlotte cannot be named the heroine of the piece, it does seem as though Jane Austen is more apt to identify with her than with Elfrida, the nominal heroine. Charlotte is the one character who travels, meets with adventure, and is described as "good-tempered," "obliging" and "lovely." While Elfrida is little more than a caricature, Charlotte is drawn more fully, and perhaps more lovingly. The hero's name, Frederic, seems to have an appeal for Austen, since it appears later in *Evelyn* and *Persuasion*. It also appears in another work of fiction, and one more closely related to Austen herself. In the marriage register in the Steventon church, she inscribed her name along with that of a Henry Frederick Howard Fitzwilliam, an imaginary and impressively named husband (Austen-Leigh, 66). Thus, in this "knockabout" tale, fact does meet fiction.

It is interesting to note Austen's treatment of marriage in this story. The goal or plot resolution of most sentimental novels is the marriage of the heroine or hero. In some cases, such as Rousseau's *Julie, ou La Nouvelle Héloïse*, marriage proves an impossibility, but the hopelessness simply adds to the sentimentalism. Here there are several marriages: both Fitzroy girls do wed but the elder marries a servant and the younger must threaten her mother with matricide should she continue to postpone the nuptials. Frederic and Elfrida become engaged for years and it is only when faced with the risk of losing her betrothed to a younger woman that Elfrida can bring herself to the altar. Frederic is certainly not the gallant hero when he proclaims, "'Damme Elfrida *you* may be married tomorrow but *I* won't.'" In general, the reader is left to wonder about the quality of these marriages as each couple is faced with either reduced finances (in the case of the coachman) or childless old age. As a mature writer, Austen would continue to leave the couple 'at the church door', allowing the reader to speculate on their happiness as they embark on married life.

It was as a parodist of the sentimental circulating-library novels that she read with such delight that Jane Austen began her writing career. Throughout the juvenilia, Austen raises parodic havoc with facile emotionalism, the cant of sentiment, the flawless hero, matchless heroine, foundling child, the exalted pedigree, the shackles of parental authority, youthful defiance, spontaneous attachment, love at first sight, tears, fainting, fantastic recognition scenes, narrative digressions, confidantes, friendships immediate and intense, forced difficulties, clichéd diction, and Gothicism. Nothing escaped her scalding wit. At the same time, her writing is moderated by reason. She makes it seem possible for playfulness and regulation to be united in harmony, without the one being sacrificed to the other.

Sylvia Hunt

Note on the Text

*F*rederic & Elfrida is the first of fourteen short stories, dramatic sketches and miscellaneous items comprising Jane Austen's manuscript notebook *Volume the First*. Austen preserved her juvenilia in three notebooks, giving them mock-solemn titles on the cover: *Volume the First, Volume the Second,* and *Volume the Third*. As Joseph Wiesenfarth observes, these titles constitute "an imitation of popular novels published in three volumes in her day—the very format in which *Sense and Sensibility, Pride and Prejudice, Mansfield Park,* and *Emma* were destined to appear in print" (Austen, *Jack & Alice,* xvi). The pieces in *Volume the First* date from as early as 1787, when Austen was eleven, to June 1793, when she was seventeen. It is possible that *Frederic & Elfrida,* the first item in the volume and written in what B.C. Southam terms "a relatively childish hand" ("The Manuscript," 232), was the earliest of all of Austen's stories.

Austen's three notebooks contain not first drafts but fair copies of lost originals, transcribed at different times. All of the notebooks also contain revisions made later than the fair copies. In some cases these revisions were written hastily, with dark ink, and occasionally alterations and additions were inserted at a much later date; *Volume the Third,* for example, contains a revision by Austen made in 1809 and new material by James Edward Austen-Leigh from the late 1820s (Austen, *Evelyn,* xviii-xx). *Volume the First,* the shabbiest of the three notebooks, is a small quarto, bound in quarter calf and marbled boards. The leather on the spine is now largely worn away, and the marbled boards are severely rubbed and faded. Mary Gaither Marshall conjectures that much of the wear occurred "during Jane Austen's life when she was writing in the volume and circulating it among family members" (114), but

Frederic & Elfrida

a novel.~

Chapter the First.

The Uncle of Elfrida was the Father of Frederic - in other words, they were first cousins by the Father's side.

Being both born in one day & both brought up at one school, it was not wonderfull that they should look on each other with something more than bare po :liteness. They loved with mutual sin: :cerity but were both determined not to Transgress the rules of Propriety by owning their attachment, either to the object beloved, or to any one else.

The first page of the manuscript of Frederic & Elfrida, *reproduced by permission of the Bodleian Library, Oxford University.*

there is no evidence for this. The front board has an ink inscription, "Volume the First," written in large letters, possibly by Austen, while the front pastedown endpaper has a pencil inscription by Austen's sister Cassandra, "For my Brother Charles."[1] Pasted to this endpaper is a scrap of paper with an ink inscription, also by Cassandra: "For my Brother Charles. I think I recollect that a few of the trifles in this Vol: were written expressly for his amusement. C.E.A." The notebook has 92 leaves, the first two unnumbered and the others paginated 1-180 by Austen. (Page 167 is misnumbered 177, and page 175 is unnumbered.) The first two unnumbered pages contain the list of contents; the third is blank. The dedication of *Frederic & Elfrida* to Martha Lloyd is on the fourth unnumbered page; the story itself is on pages 1-21.

On Austen's death in 1817, the three notebooks were preserved by Cassandra and later, probably on her death in 1845, were given to different family members. *Volume the First* went, as Cassandra intended, to her younger brother Charles and remained in his family, passing down to his eldest daughter, Cassandra Esten, and then to the daughters of his son Charles John. Three of these daughters—the impoverished spinsters Jane, Emma Florence, and Blanche Frederica—sold various Austen manuscripts in the 1920s, including *Volume the First*. In November 1932, its whereabouts was discovered by R.W. Chapman, who arranged for it to be bought for the Bodleian Library, Oxford, by the Friends of the Bodleian. The sale was completed in January 1933, when the Friends wrote a cheque for £75, made out to H. Deacon but sent to Gerald Goodwin at Leigh Rectory, Stoke-on-Trent. Chapman retained possession of the notebook for several months, until the annual meeting of the Friends in June 1933. This gave him time to edit the work; his edition was published by the Clarendon Press in time for the June meeting. The text of *Volume the First* is

---

1   In his edition of *Volume the First* (1933), R.W. Chapman declares that this pencilled note is "doubtless in Jane Austen's hand (certainly not in that of her sister Cassandra" (xvii). Both David Gilson (383) and Mary Marshall (114), however, believe that the hand is Cassandra's, and I find the hands of the pencilled note and the ink inscription pasted on a scrap of paper very similar.

also that in Chapman's edition of Austen's *Minor Works*, first published in 1954 and still in print, with textual revisions and additional notes by Brian Southam.

The text of the present edition of *Frederic & Elfrida* follows Austen's manuscript as closely as possible. No changes have been made to spelling, capitalization, paragraphing, or punctuation, and the ampersand symbol has been retained. Our text thus differs from those in the three previous editions—by Chapman, Frances Beer, and Margaret Anne Doody and Douglas Murray—all of which are standardized and modernized in various ways. Our aim is to convey the full flavour of the youthful Austen's stylistic idiosyncrasies which, while transgressing the rules of spelling and punctuation, pose no problems of comprehension. For all words or phrases deleted, added, or revised, the original reading is recorded in textual notes at the foot of the page. There are few such alterations (ten in all) in *Frederic & Elfrida*, which is among the more lightly revised stories among Austen's juvenilia. References to Austen's juvenilia in the Introduction and Explanatory Notes are to separate Juvenilia Press editions, when they exist; other references to Austen are to Chapman's editions of the novels and minor works and Le Faye's edition of the letters.

Peter Sabor

Cast of Characters

FREDERIC FALKNOR, our hero, in love with Elfrida, but...;

ELFRIDA FALKNOR, our heroine, in love with Frederic, but...;

CHARLOTTE DRUMMOND, their friend, the girl who can't say no;

Mrs. WILLIAMSON of Portland Place, her aunt;

JEZALINDA FITZROY, neighbour and friend, fond of the Coachman;

REBECCA FITZROY, her sister, fond of Captain Roger;

Aged Gentleman, fond of Charlotte;

Young & Handsome Gentleman, also fond of Charlotte;

ELEANOR ROGERS, pretty daughter to Rebecca and Captain Roger.

They loved with mutual sincerity but...

To Miss Lloyd[1]

My dear Martha,
As a small testimony of the gratitude I feel for your late generosity to me in finishing my muslin[a] Cloak,[2] I beg leave to offer you this little production of your sincere Freind
The Author

Frederic & Elfrida
a novel

————————————
Chapter the First
————————————

The Uncle of Elfrida was the Father[b] of Frederic; in other words, they were first cousins by the Father's side.[3]

Being both born in one day & both brought up at one school, it was not wonderfull[4] that they should look on each other with something more than bare politeness.[5c] They loved with mutual sincerity but were both determined not to transgress the rules of Propriety by owning their attachment, either to the object beloved, or[d] to any one else.[6]

They were exceedingly handsome and so much alike, that it was not every one who knew them apart. Nay even their most intimate freinds had nothing to distinguish them by, but the shape of the face, the colour of the Eye, the length

———————————

a   "muslin" inserted above line.
b   "Mother" deleted; "Father" inserted above.
c   "politenness" corrected to "politeness."
d   "either to the object beloved, or" inserted above line.

...determined not to transgress the rules of Propriety

of the Nose & the difference of the complexion.[7]

Elfrida had an intimate freind to whom, being on a visit to an Aunt, she wrote the following Letter.

To Miss Drummond
"Dear Charlotte

I should be obliged to you if you would buy me, during your stay with Mrs Williamson, a new & fashionable Bonnet,[8] to suit the Complexion of your

E. Falknor"

Charlotte, whose character was a willingness to oblige every one, when she returned into the Country, brought her Freind the wished-for Bonnet, & so ended this little adventure, much to the satisfaction of all parties.

On her return to Crankhumdunberry (of which sweet village[9] her father was Rector) Charlotte was received with the greatest Joy by Frederic & Elfrida, who, after pressing her alternately to their Bosoms, proposed to her to take a walk in a Grove of Poplars which led from the Parsonage to a verdant Lawn enamelled with a variety of variegated flowers & watered by a purling Stream, brought from the Valley

...pressing her alternately to their Bosoms...

A walk in a Grove of Poplars

of Tempé[10] by a passage under ground.

In this Grove they had scarcely remained above 9 hours, when they were suddenly agreably surprized by hearing a most delightfull voice warble the following stanza.

Song

That Damon[11] was in love with me
I once thought & beleiv'd
But now that he is not I see,
I fear I was deceiv'd.

No sooner were the lines finished than they beheld by a turning in the Grove 2 elegant young women leaning on each other's arm, who immediately on perceiving them, took a different path & disappeared from their sight.

Chapter the Second

As Elfrida & her companions, had seen enough of them to know that they were neither the 2 Miss Greens, nor Mrs Jackson & her Daughter, they could not help expressing their surprise at their appearance; till at length recollecting, that a new family had lately taken a House not far from the Grove, they hastened home, determined to lose no time in forming an acquaintance with 2 such amiable & worthy Girls, of which family they rightly imagined them^e to be a part.

Agreable to such a determination, they went that very evening to pay their respects to Mrs Fitzroy & her two Daughters. On being shewn into an elegant dressing room, ornamented with festoons of artificial flowers,[12] they were struck with the engaging Exterior & beautifull outside of Jezalinda the eldest of the young Ladies; but e'er they had been many minutes seated, the Wit & Charms which shone resplendant in the conversation of the amiable Rebecca, enchanted them so much that they all with one accord jumped up & exclaimed.

"Lovely & too charming Fair one, notwithstanding your forbidding Squint, your greazy tresses & your swelling Back, which are more frightfull than imagination can paint or pen describe, I cannot refrain from expressing my raptures, at

---

e   "them" inserted above line.

Lovely & too charming Fair one

the engaging Qualities of your Mind, which so amply atone for the Horror, with which your first appearance must ever inspire the unwary visitor."[13]

"Your sentiments so nobly expressed on the different excellencies of Indian & English Muslins,[14] & the judicious preference you give the former, have excited in me an admiration of which I can alone give an adequate idea, by assuring you it is nearly equal to what I feel for myself."

Then making a profound Curtesy to the amiable & abashed Rebecca, they left the room & hurried home.

From this period, the intimacy between the Families of Fitzroy, Drummond, and Falknor, daily encreased till at length it grew to such a pitch, that they did not scruple to kick one another out of the window on the slightest provocation.

During this happy state of Harmony, the eldest Miss Fitzroy ran off with the Coachman[15] & the amiable Rebecca was asked in marriage by Captain Roger of Buckinghamshire.[16]

Mrs Fitzroy did not approve of the match on account of the tender years of the young couple, Rebecca being but 36 & Captain Roger little more than 63.[17] To remedy this objection, it was agreed that they should wait a little while till they were a good deal older.

Chapter the Third

In the mean time the parents of Frederic proposed to those of Elfrida, an union between them, which being accepted with pleasure, the wedding cloathes were bought & nothing remained to be settled but the naming of the Day.

As to the lovely Charlotte, being importuned with eagerness to pay another visit to her Aunt, she determined to accept the invitation & in consequence of it walked to Mrs Fitzroys to take leave of the amiable Rebecca, whom she found surrounded by Patches,^f Powder, Pomatum & Paint[18] with which she was vainly endeavouring to remedy the natural plainness of her face.

"I am come my amiable Rebecca, to take my leave of you

---

f   "Rouge" deleted; "Patches" inserted above.

...the wedding cloathes were bought

for the fortnight I am destined to spend with my aunt.
Beleive me this separation is painfull to me, but it is as nec-
essary as the labour which now engages you."

"Why to tell you the truth my Love, replied Rebecca, I
have lately taken it into my head to think (perhaps with
little reason) that my complexion is by no means equal to
the rest of my face & have therefore taken, as you see, to

Seated in the most affectionate manner in one chair

white & red paint, which I would scorn to use on any other occasion as I hate art."

Charlotte, who perfectly understood the meaning of her freind's speech, was too goodtemper'd & obliging to refuse her, what she knew she wished,—a compliment; & they parted the best freinds in the world.

With a heavy heart & streaming Eyes did she ascend the lovely vehicle[g][19] which bore her from her freinds & home; but greived as she was, she little thought in what a strange & different manner she should[h] return to it.

---

g   a post-chaise [Austen's note]

h   "would" deleted; "should" inserted above.

On her entrance into the city of London which was the place of Mrs Williamson's abode, the postilion,[20] whose stupidity was amazing, declared & declared even without the least shame or Compunction, that having never been informed he was totally ignorant of what part of the Town, he was to drive to.

Charlotte, whose nature we have before intimated, was an earnest desire to oblige every one, with the greatest Condescension & Good humour informed him that he was to drive to Portland Place,[21] which he accordingly did^i & Charlotte soon found herself in the arms of a fond Aunt.

Scarcely were they seated as usual, in the most affectionate manner in one chair,[22] than the Door suddenly opened & an aged gentleman with a sallow face & old pink Coat,[23] partly by intention & partly thro' weakness was at the feet of the lovely Charlotte, declaring his attachment to her & beseeching her pity in the most moving manner.

---

i   "did" inserted above line.

...intreated permission to pay to her, his addresses

Not being able to resolve to make any one miserable, she consented to become his wife; where upon the Gentleman left the room & all was quiet.

Their quiet however continued but a short time, for on a second opening of the door a young & Handsome Gentleman with a new blue coat,[24] entered & intreated from the lovely Charlotte, permission to pay to her, his addresses. There was a something in the appearance of the second Stranger, that influenced Charlotte in his favour, to the full as much as the appearance of the first: she could not account for it,[25] but so it was.

Having therefore agreable to that & the natural turn of her mind to make every one happy, promised to become his Wife the next morning, he took his leave & the two Ladies sat down to Supper on a young Leveret,[26] a brace of Partridges, a leash of Pheasants[27] & a Dozen of Pigeons.

Chapter the Fourth

It was not till the next morning that Charlotte recollected the double engagement she had entered into; but when she did, the reflection of her past folly, operated so strongly on her mind, that she resolved to be guilty of a greater, & to that end threw herself into a deep stream which ran thro' her Aunts pleasure Grounds[28] in Portland Place.

She floated to Crankhumdunberry where she was picked up & buried; the following epitaph, composed by Frederic Elfrida & Rebecca, was placed on her tomb.

Epitaph
Here lies our freind who having promis-ed
That unto two she would be marri-ed

Threw her sweet Body & her lovely face
Into the Stream that runs thro' Portland Place

These sweet lines, as pathetic as beautifull were never read by any one who passed that way, without a shower of tears, which if they should fail of exciting in you, Reader, your mind must be unworthy to peruse them.

Having performed the last sad office to their departed freind, Frederic & Elfrida together with Captain Roger & Rebecca returned to Mrs Fitzroy's at whose feet they threw themselves with one accord & addressed her in the following Manner.

"Madam

"When the sweet Captain Roger first[j] addressed the amiable Rebecca, you alone objected to their union on account of the tender years of the Parties. That plea can be no more, seven days being now expired, together with the lovely Char-

---

j   "most" (?) deleted; "first" inserted above, in a later hand, in dark ink.

lotte,[29] since the Captain first spoke to you on the subject.

"Consent then Madam to their union & as a reward, this smelling Bottle which I enclose in my right hand, shall be yours & yours forever; I never will claim it again. But if you refuse to join their hands in 3 days time, this dagger[30] which I enclose in my left shall be steeped in your hearts blood.

"Speak then Madam & decide their fate & yours."

Such gentle & sweet persuasion could not fail of having the desired effect. The answer they received, was this.

"My dear young freinds

"The arguments you have used are too just & too eloquent to be withstood; Rebecca in 3 days time, you shall be united to the Captain."

This speech, than which nothing could be more satisfactory, was received with Joy by all; & peace being once more restored on all sides, Captain Roger intreated Rebecca to favour them with a Song, in compliance with which request having first assured them that she had a terrible cold, she sung as follows.

Song
When Corydon[31] went to the fair
    He bought a red ribbon for Bess,
With which she encircled her hair
    & made herself look very fess.[32]

The Cloathes grew out of fashion

Chapter the fifth

At the end of 3 days Captain Roger and Rebecca were united and immediately after the Ceremony set off in the Stage Waggon[33] for the Captain's seat in Buckinghamshire.

The parents of Elfrida, alltho' they earnestly wished to see her married to Frederic before they died, yet knowing the delicate frame of her mind could ill bear the least excertion & rightly judging that naming her wedding day would be too great a one, forebore to press her on the subject.

Weeks & Fortnights flew away without gaining the least ground; the Cloathes grew out of fashion & at length Capt. Roger & his Lady arrived to pay a visit to their Mother & introduce to her their beautifull Daughter of eighteen.

Elfrida, who had found her former acquaintance were growing too old & too ugly to be any longer agreable, was rejoiced to hear of the arrival of so pretty a girl as Eleanor with whom she determined to form the strictest freindship.

But the Happiness she had expected from an acquaintance with Eleanor, she soon found was not to be received, for she had not only the mortification of finding herself treated by her as little less than an old woman, but had actually the horror of perceiving a growing passion in the Bosom of Frederic for the Daughter of the amiable Rebecca.

The instant she had the first idea of such an attachment, she flew to Frederic & in a manner truly heroick, spluttered out to him her intention of being married the next Day.

To one in his predicament who possessed less personal Courage than Frederic was master of, such a speech would have been Death; but he not being the least terrified boldly replied,

Perceiving a growing passion in the Bosom of Frederic

"Damme Elfrida—<u>you</u> may be married to-morrow but <u>I</u> won't."

This answer distressed her too much for her delicate Constitution. She accordingly fainted & was in such a hurry to have a succession of fainting fits, that she had scarcely patience enough to recover from one before she fell into another.[34]

Tho', in any threatening Danger to his Life or Liberty, Frederic was as bold as brass yet in other respects his heart was as soft as cotton & immediately on hearing of the dangerous way Elfrida was in, he flew to her & finding her better than he had been taught to expect, was united to her Forever —.

———
Finis.
———

Explanatory Notes

1. Miss Lloyd: Martha Lloyd (1765-1843), with her sisters Eliza and Mary, was a friend and neighbour of JA at Steventon. Much later, in 1828, she would become the second wife of JA's brother Francis. Southam observes that this dedication "is remarkable for being in a later hand than that in which the rest of the piece is written" ("The Manuscript," 232, n. 4).

2. muslin Cloak: JA's interest in muslin, a fashionable finely woven cotton, appears in *Northanger Abbey*, where Henry Tilney displays a surprising expertise on the subject (I, iii). Martha Lloyd, seven years older than JA, had apparently aided her in sewing a muslin cloak, which would be worn indoors. *Frederic & Elfrida* also features an expert on muslins; see below, note 14. In inserting the word "muslin" above the line here, JA creates a link between the dedication to Martha Lloyd and the characters in her story.

3. the Father's side: Frederic and Elfrida thus have the same surname, Falknor, as Elfrida signs herself in her letter to Miss Drummond below. Had they been cousins on the mother's side, as JA seems originally to have intended, their surnames would have been different.

4. wonderfull: The suffix -*full*, as Southam observes ("The Manuscript," 236), appears frequently in JA's earliest juvenilia, but not in the later items in *Volume the First* or, generally, in the other two notebooks. The most prominent example is in the title of JA's *The Beautifull Cassandra*.

5   bare politeness: Marriages between first cousins were frequent in JA's time. In Emily Brontë's *Wuthering Heights* (1847), set in the late-eighteenth and early-nineteenth century, the second Catherine marries first a paternal cousin, Linton Heathcliff (in 1801) and then a maternal one, Hareton Earnshaw (in 1803). In *Mansfield Park*, Mrs Norris assures Sir Thomas Bertram that "the only sure way of providing against" a marriage between one of his sons, Tom or Edmund, and their maternal cousin, Fanny Price, is to "breed her up with them" (6-7). Although Sir Thomas follows this advice, Fanny does, of course, eventually marry Edmund.

6. rules of Propriety ... any one else: Such restraint on the part of Frederic

and Elfrida goes beyond standard conventions of propriety. Even Arabella, the excessively romantic heroine of Charlotte Lennox's satirical novel *The Female Quixote* (1752), criticizes a romance heroine "who was so rigid and austere, that she thought all Expressions of Love were criminal; and was so far from granting any Person Permission to love her, that she thought it a mortal Offence to be adored even in private" (89). JA heightened the comedy by adding the phrase "either to the object beloved"; in the original reading, Frederic and Elfrida's determination to conceal their love only from others is more conventional. In an essay in Samuel Johnson's *The Rambler* (97, 19 February 1751) that JA quotes in *Northanger Abbey* (29-30), Samuel Richardson writes: "That a young lady should be in love, and the love of the young gentleman undeclared, is an heterodoxy which prudence, and even policy, must not allow" (156). The lady, however, "perhaps is not an absolute stranger to the passion of the young gentleman."

7. **so much alike ... complexion**: JA's satire of the convention whereby lovers should resemble each other—here the two are utterly unlike—recurs in *A Collection of Letters*, in which Lady Scudamore assures Henrietta that she and her beloved Musgrove are "born for each other ... your opinions and Sentiments so exactly coincide. Nay, the colour of your Hair is not very different" (25).

8. **fashionable Bonnet**: In *The Beautifull Cassandra*, the heroine chances "to fall in love with an elegant Bonnet" (ch. ii). Juliet McMaster notes that the bonnet here, "after Cassandra herself, is the most important character in the story" and that "falling in love with bonnets became a standing joke" between Jane and her sister Cassandra ("Afterword About Jane Austen").

9. **Crankhumdunberry ... sweet village**: an echo, as Doody and Murray note (288), of Oliver Goldsmith's "The Deserted Village" (1770), l. 1: "Sweet Auburn, loveliest village of the plain." "Crankhumdunberry" is a mock-Irish name, but the story has an English setting and there are no other references to Ireland. JA uses other such place names in the juvenilia: the mock-Welsh Pammydiddle in *Jack & Alice* and mock-Irish Kilhoobery Park in *Sir William Mountague*.

10. **Valley of Tempé**: The highly poetic "purling Stream" runs a most improbable underground course from the celebrated valley in Greece, formerly a shrine to Apollo. In *The Female Quixote*, Arabella compares the situation of Bath, placed in a valley, with Tempé, of which her companions have never heard (259).

11. **Damon**: a shepherd singer in Virgil's eighth eclogue, whose name was adoped by English poets such as Milton and Marvell for rural lovers.

12 . artificial flowers: popular when worn on hats, as hair ornaments, or as nosegays, but fresh flowers would be expected in an "elegant dressing room."

13 . Lovely ... unwary visitor: In a panel discussion on the juvenilia transcribed in *Jane Austen's Beginnings*, ed. Grey, Jan Fergus singles out this sentence for special praise: "My brother loved that; my students love that. It's just wonderful" (235).

14 . Indian & English Muslins: Muslin imported from India was more expensive and generally considered superior to that produced domestically. In *Northanger Abbey* (74), JA refers to "mull" and "jackonet": two varieties of Indian muslin.

15 . the eldest Miss Fitzroy ran off with the Coachman: an outrageous lapse in gentility, even worse than eloping with the butler, as does Miss Dickins, the governess of the youthful Lady Williams in *Jack & Alice* (11). In Sterne's *Tristram Shandy* (1759-67), the fact that Tristram's great-aunt Dinah "about sixty years ago, was married and got with child by the coachman" is a subject so painfully embarrassing to her nephew Toby that "The least hint of it was enough to make the blood fly into his face" (I, xxi).

16 . Buckinghamshire: A county in the south of England, east of Oxfordshire and north of JA's native Hampshire.

17 . Rebecca being but 36 ... more than 63: Elsewhere JA varies the joke, with characters perceiving the relatively youthful as exceedingly aged. In *The Three Sisters*, Miss Stanhope describes her suitor Mr Watts as "quite an old Man, about two & thirty" (18). In *Sense and Sensibility*, Marianne Dashwood regards Colonel Brandon as, at 35, "an old bachelor" and declares that a woman of 27 "can never hope to feel or inspire affection again" (37-38).

18 . Patches, Powder, Pomatum & Paint: echoing, as Doody and Murray note, a line in Pope's "The Rape of the Lock": "Puffs, Powder, Patches, Bibles, Billet-doux" (I, 139). JA originally wrote "Rouge, Powder," etc.; in changing "Rouge" to "Patches," she created both the quadruple alliteration and the Pope allusion. In contrast to Pope's heroine Belinda, who makes good use of the battery on her dressing-table ("Now awful Beauty puts on all its Arms"), plain Rebecca here cannot be beautified by cosmetics. Black patches, made of velvet, were supposed to resemble beauty-spots, and remained fashionable until c. 1790. Powder was used for colouring hair; pomatum, an oil-based dressing, kept hair plastered in place; white paint was applied to the neck and red paint (rouge) to the cheeks, but the use of both colours declined in the 1780s.

19 . the lovely vehicle: JA's note, "A post-chaise," explains why Charlotte's car-

riage is "lovely": this was the most expensive and luxurious type of hired carriage. A post-chaise generally carried only two passengers and travelled rapidly, in contrast to the much cheaper and slower stage-waggon used by Captain Roger and Rebecca (17). JA's notes in her own fiction are extremely rare; another example is her note in *Northanger Abbey*, citing Richardson's essay in *The Rambler* (see note 6 above).

20 . **postilion**: the driver, mounted on the "near" (left) horse of the team drawing the post-chaise. Postilions also served as attendants during a journey. A chaise and four, such as that owned by General Tilney, had two postilions, mounted on the two near horses, "handsomely liveried, rising so regularly in their stirrups" (*Northanger Abbey*, 156). A larger carriage, such as Captain Roger and Rebecca's stage-waggon, would have a driver mounted on a box at the front of the vehicle.

21 . **Portland Place**: a magnificently wide street in Westminster, laid out in about 1778, and the most fashionable address in London.

22 . **seated ... in one chair**: Sitting two to a chair also features in JA's comedy "The Visit," in which Lady Hampton takes her husband Sir Arthur in her lap, and Sophy Hampton takes Lord Fitzgerald in hers (52).

23 . **old pink Coat**: The colour of this foolish suitor's coat denotes his foppish character. In Smollett's *Roderick Random* (1748), the effete Captain Whiffle wears a coat of "pink-coloured silk, lined with white" (195); in JA's *Mansfield Park*, Mr Rushworth is to wear a "pink satin cloak" as Count Cassel in *Lovers' Vows* (138). In a letter to Cassandra of 9 January 1796 (her earliest surviving letter) JA declares that Tom Lefroy "has but *one* fault, which time will, I trust, entirely remove—it is that his morning coat is a great deal too light" (2). Lefroy, she continues, "is a very great admirer of Tom Jones, and therefore wears the same coloured clothes ... which *he* did when he was wounded": Fielding's hero wears a white coat that shows his blood "very visibly" (VII, xix). A few days later, in a letter to Cassandra of 14 January 1796, JA mockingly threatens to refuse an offer of marriage from Tom Lefroy "unless he promises to give away his white Coat" (3). In *Jack & Alice*, the remarkably handsome Charles Adams wears a "plain green Coat" (5).

24 . **new blue coat**: As Doody and Murray note (319), blue was a favourite colour of JA's. In *Pride and Prejudice* (9), Bingley, also young and handsome, likewise wears a blue coat.

25 . **something in the appearance ... she could not account for it**: The elaborate mystification satirizes a recurring debate in courtship protocol about whether "person" or physical attractiveness ought to influence a modest

girl in her choice of a husband. In Richardson's *Sir Charles Grandison* (1753-54), Harriet Byron's love for Sir Charles, although unrequited, is deemed worthy, since "the *mind* and not the *person* is the principal object of [her] love" (I, 304).

26 . Leveret: a young, and therefore tender hare.

27 . brace ... Pheasants: i.e. two partridges and three pheasants.

28 . deep stream ... pleasure Grounds: Houses in Portland Place did not, of course, possess "pleasure Grounds," which would require considerable space, or streams of any kind.

29 . seven days ... expired, together with the lovely Charlotte: Syllepsis, a form of zeugma in which a verb takes two different and incongruous objects, is a favourite rhetorical device of the young JA. In *Jack & Alice*, the story that follows *Frederic & Elfrida* in *Volume the First*, Alice exclaims, after Lucy's leg has been broken by Charles Adams's man-trap, "Oh! cruel Charles to wound the hearts & legs of all the fair" (17). In *Lesley Castle*, Charlotte Lutterell writes of her sister, "She loved drawing Pictures, and I drawing [disembowelling] Pullets" (28).

30 . smelling Bottle ... dagger: a parody of the traditional choice between dagger and bowl. In Joseph Addison's *Rosamond an Opera* (1707), Queen Elinor gives her rival Rosamond the choice of committing suicide by drinking poison from a bowl or being stabbed by a dagger. Smelling bottles, small and ornamental, contained smelling-salts, used as a restorative in case of faintness, headaches, etc.

31 . Corydon: like Damon above, a traditional name for a rustic lover in pastoral poetry, deriving from a shepherd so named in the *Idylls* of Theocritus and the *Eclogues* of Virgil. JA also gives the name to a character in her brief comedy, "The Mystery," who speaks no more than the opening line.

32 . fess: a dialect term for lively, gay, smart.

33 . Stage Waggon: the cheapest, slowest and least comfortable form of public transport, and thus especially inappropriate for newly-weds. Passengers sat on benches in this very large conveyance, drawn by eight horses, which would proceed at walking pace.

34 . fainting fits ... another: These spectacular fainting fits prefigure those of Laura and Sophia in JA's *Love and Freindship*, which includes the famous remark, "We fainted alternately on a Sofa" (12). In his continuation of JA's *Evelyn*, James Edward Austen-Leigh also has the hero, Mr Gower, faint on a sofa (16).

Illustrator's Note

I n defiance of the Unity of Time (as of all other rules of prob
ability whatever) young Jane Austen in *Frederic & Elfrida*
calls for some twenty years to pass in the middle of a breath-
lessly brief narrative. Between falling in love, getting engaged,
and getting married, our hero and heroine, Frederic and Elfrida,
linger through the courtship and marriage of their friend Rebecca,
and the growing up of Rebecca's daughter into a seductive eight-
een-year-old whose youthful charms tempt the now ageing
Frederic.

Once Elfrida and Frederic overcome their scruples of Propriety
sufficiently to become engaged, "the wedding cloathes were bought
& nothing remained to be settled but the naming of the Day."
This new issue in punctilio, the naming of the day, keeps the
romance stalled while "Weeks & Fortnights flew away ... the
Cloathes grew out of fashion."

As an illustrator, I wanted to make the most of this hiatus of
passing decades and changing fashions between the buying of the
wedding clothes and the final consummation. I thought of those
wedding clothes as something like Miss Havisham's outfit in *Great
Expectations*, a visible reminder of the ravages of time and propriety.

If we can plausibly date the end of the story as close to Austen's
completion of composition, in the late 1780s, then one may sup-
pose that Frederic and Elfrida fall in love around 1770: call it
Evelina time, the time of wigs for men, and elaborate hairdos,
panniers, and wide skirts for women: a far cry from the Empire
waistline and flimsy muslins of the Regency that we usually asso-
ciate with Jane Austen's mature fiction.

But in this outrageous tale everything is overstated - like

Rebecca's appearance with "forbidding Squint, ... greazy Tresses & ... swelling Back." And I take the liberty to overstate the change in fashions too. My Frederic and Elfrida would already be a little out of fashion in 1770; and my nubile Eleanor would be considerably *ahead* of the fashion in 1790.

But let me assure you that my artistic licence, like young Jane's, is signed and sealed.

Juliet Muhmaster

Works Cited

Austen, Jane. *Amelia Webster and The Three Sisters*. Ed. Juliet McMaster et al. Edmonton: Juvenilia Press, 1993.

———. *The Beautifull Cassandra*. Ed. Juliet McMaster. Victoria, B.C.: Sono Nis Press, 1993.

———. *Catharine and Other Writings*. Ed. Margaret Anne Doody and Douglas Murray. Oxford: Oxford World's Classics, 1993.

———. *A Collection of Letters*. Ed. Juliet McMaster et al. Edmonton: Juvenilia Press, 1998.

———. *Evelyn*. Ed Peter Sabor et al. Edmonton: Juvenilia Press, 1999.

———. *Jack & Alice*. Ed. Joseph Wiesenfarth et al. Edmonton: Juvenilia Press, 2001.

———. *Jane Austen's Letters*. Ed. Deirdre Le Faye. Oxford: Oxford University Press, 1995.

——— *Love & Freindship*. Ed. Juliet McMaster et al. Edmonton: Juvenilia Press, 1995

———. *Minor Works*. Ed. R.W. Chapman. London: Oxford University Press, 1954; rev. by B.C. Southam, 1969.

———. *The Novels of Jane Austen*. Ed. R.W. Chapman, 5 vols. 3rd edition. London: Oxford University Press, 1965-67.

———. *Volume the First*. Ed. R.W. Chapman. Oxford: Clarendon Press, 1933; London: Athlone Press, 1984.

Austen-Leigh, James Edward. *A Memoir of Jane Austen*. 2nd ed. Ed. R.W. Chapman. Oxford: Oxford University Press, 1951.

Beer, Frances, ed. *The Juvenilia of Jane Austen and Charlotte Brontë*. Harmondsworth: Penguin, 1986.

Brophy, Brigid. "Jane Austen and the Stuarts." In *Critical Essays on Jane Austen*, ed. B.C. Southam. London: Routledge, 1968. 21-38.

Fielding, Sarah. *The Adventures of David Simple* and *Volume the Last*. Ed. Peter Sabor. Lexington: University Press of Kentucky, 1998.

Gilson, David. *A Bibliography of Jane Austen*. Oxford: Clarendon Press, 1982.

Grey, J. David, ed. *Jane Austen's Beginnings: The Juvenilia and* Lady Susan. Ann Arbor: U.M.I. Press, 1989.

Lennox, Charlotte. *The Female Quixote*. Ed. Margaret Dalziel. Oxford: Oxford University Press, 1970.

Litz, A. Walton. "Jane Austen: The Juvenilia." In Grey, ed., *Jane Austen's Beginnings*. 1-6.

Marshall, Mary Gaither. "Jane Austen's Manuscripts of the Juvenilia and *Lady Susan*: A History and Description." In Grey, ed., *Jane Austen's Beginnings*. 107-21.

Nokes, David. *Jane Austen: A Life*. London: Fourth Estate, 1997.

Richardson, Samuel. *Clarissa*. Ed. Angus Ross. London: Penguin, 1985.

———. Essay no. 97 (19 February 1751). In Samuel Johnson, *The Rambler*, ed. W.J. Bate and Albrecht B. Strauss, The Yale Edition of the Works of Samuel Johnson, IV (New Haven: Yale University Press, 1969), 153-59.

———. *Sir Charles Grandison*. Ed. Jocelyn Harris. 3 vols. London: Oxford University Press, 1972.

Smollett, Tobias. *The Adventures of Roderick Random*. Ed. Paul-Gabriel Boucé. Oxford: Oxford University Press, 1979.

Southam, B.C. *Jane Austen's Literary Manuscripts*. Oxford: Clarendon Press, 1964.

———. "The Manuscript of Jane Austen's "Volume the First.'" *The Library*, 5th ser., 17 (1962), 231-37.

Catalogue

The Juvenilia Press is an enterprise that combines scholarship with pedagogy. It is designed to publish editions of early works of known writers, in a simple format, with student involvement. Each volume, besides the text by the young author (of any age up to 20), includes light-hearted illustration, scholarly annotation, and an introduction that relates this work to the author's mature writing. It thus provides an opportunity for scholars and apprentice scholars to collaborate in editing the apprentice work of their authors. Available volumes are priced between $4 and $8.

GENERAL EDITOR: Juliet McMaster

VOLUMES IN THE SERIES, WITH PRINCIPAL EDITORS:
- *Jack & Alice*, by Jane Austen at about 13.
- *The Twelve Adventurers: A Romance*, by Charlotte Brontë at 13.
- *Amelia Webster and The Three Sisters*, by Jane Austen at c. 13 and 16.
- *Indamora to Lindamira*, by Lady Mary Pierrepont (later Wortley Montagu), at about 14, edited by Isobel Grundy. First publication.
- *Norna, or the Witch's Curse*, by Louisa May Alcott at about 15.
- *Pockets Full of Stars*, by Alison White, edited by Arlette Zinck.
- *Branwell's Blackwood's Magazine*, by Branwell Brontë at 11, edited by Christine Alexander. First publication.
- *The History of England*, by Jane Austen at 15, edited by Jan Fergus.
- *Love and Freindship*, by Jane Austen at 14, edited by Juliet McMaster.
- *Edward Neville*, by George Eliot at 14, edited by Juliet McMaster.
- *Catharine, or The Bower*, by Jane Austen at 16, edited by Juliet McMaster.
- *Henry and Eliza*, by Jane Austen at about 13.
- *A Quiet Game*, by Margaret Atwood at about 17. Edited by Kathy Chung and Sherrill Grace. First publication.

Catalogue

- *The Young Visiters*, by Daisy Ashford at 9. Edited by Juliet McMaster and others. (Not available for sale)
- *My Angria and the Angrians*, by Charlotte Brontë at 18, edited by Juliet McMaster, Leslie Robertson and others.
- *Embryo Words*, by Margaret Laurence. Edited by Nora Foster Stovel.
- *A Collection of Letters*, by Jane Austen at about 16. Edited by Juliet McMaster and others.
- *Lesley Castle*, by Jane Austen at c. 15. Edited by Jan Fergus and others.
- *Satan in a Barrel, and other early stories*, by Malcolm Lowry. Edited by Sherrill Grace.
- *Evelyn*, by Jane Austen. Edited by Peter Sabor and others.
- *Albion and Marina*, by Charlotte Brontë. Edited by Juliet McMaster and others.
- *Colors of Speech*, by Margaret Laurence. Edited by Nora Foster Stovel. First Publication.
- *The Adventurer*, by Lady Mary Pierrepont at 14. Edited by Isobel Grundy. First Publication.
- *Early Voices*, by Greg Hollingshead, Carol Shields, Aritha van Herk and Rudy Wiebe. Edited by T. L. Walters and James King.
- *Jack & Alice*, by Jane Austen at about 13. Edited by Joseph Wiesenfarth and others.
- *Peter Paul Rubens and Other Friendly Folk*, by Opal Whiteley. Edited by Laura Cappello, Juliet McMaster, Lesley Peterson and Chris Wangler.s
- *Tales of the Islanders*, by Charlotte Brontë. Edited by Christine Alexander and others.
- *Sunbeams from a Golden Machine*, by Marian Engel. Edited by Afra Kavanagh and Tammy MacNeil.
- *Frederic & Elfrida*, by Jane Austen. Edited by Peter Sabor and others.

Editorial Teams

Jack and Alice, by Jane Austen
1992, reprinted 1994. Introduction: Tara Hamelin. Annotations: Kirstin Jeffrey. Illustrations: Joyce Mandamin, Juliet McMaster, June Menzies, Bruce Venne.

The Twelve Adventurers, by Charlotte Brontë
1993, reprinted 1994. Introduction: John Barach and Laura Stovel. Annotations: John Barach. Illustrations: Karen Chow, June Menzies, Juliet McMaster. Editorial assistance: Fatima Hussein, Chantell Perrott, Betty Ann Schendler.

Amelia Webster and The Three Sisters, by Jane Austen
1993, reprinted 1995. Introduction and Annotations: Michael Londry and Beth Salter-Petersen. Illustrations: June Menzies, Carolyn Pounder, Jennifer Sthankiya. Editorial assistance: Erika Danis, Tanis Grimoldby, Margaret Holden, Maureen Spencer, Nicholette Walker.

Indamora to Lindamira, by Lady Mary Wortley Montagu
1994, edited by Isobel Grundy. Annotations: Susan Hillabold. Illustrations: Juliet McMaster.

Norna, or the Witch's Curse, by Louisa May Alcott
1994. Introduction and Annotations: Nicole Lafrenière, Catriona Martyn, Erika Rothwell. Text and textual history: Michael Londry. Illustrations: Karen Chow, Shannon Goetze. Editorial assistance: Liana Henkel, Jennifer McGregor.

Pockets Full of Stars, by Alison White
1994. Edited by Arlette Zinck. Illustrations: Shannon Goetze.

Branwell's Blackwood's Magazine, by Branwell Brontë
with contributions by his sister, Charlotte Brontë
1995. Edited by Christine Alexander, assisted by Vanessa Benson. Illustrations: Rebecca Alexander. Design: Winston Pei.

The History of England, by Jane Austen
1995. Edited by Jan Fergus. Annotations: Jennifer M. Bailey, Theodore A. Blaisdell, Mary Kate Boland, Anne M. Dickson, Melissa Fiesta, Kathleen Mosher, Peter A. Puchek, Stacy Stainbrook, R.J. Stangherlin, Jill A. Wozniak. Illustrations: Cassandra Austen and Juliet McMaster.

Editorial Teams

Love and Freindship, by Jane Austen
1995. Edited by Juliet McMaster. Introduction: Pippa Brush. Textual editing: Winston Pei and Christopher Wiebe. Illustrations: Sherry Klein. Annotations: Rachel Bennett, Pippa Brush, Shelley Galliah, Sherry Klein, Victoria Lamont, Marg McCutcheon, Juliet McMaster, Richard Pickard, Tania Smith, Christopher Wiebe. Design: Winston Pei.

Edward Neville, by George Eliot
1995. Edited by Juliet McMaster. Text: Bonnie Herron, Tania Smith. Annotations: Bonnie Herron, Juliet McMaster, Tania Smith, Sherryl Vint, Nicholette Walker, Lisa Ward. Illustrations: Juliet McMaster, Karys Van de Pitte. Historical afterword: Tania Smith.

Catharine, or the Bower, by Jane Austen
1996. Edited by Juliet McMaster. Introduction: Jeffrey Herrle. Textual editing: Joanna Denford, Jeffrey Herrle, Janice Schroeder. Annotations: Joanna Denford, Jeffrey Herrle, Bonnie Herron, Juliet McMaster, Leslie Robertson, Janice Schroeder, Pam Stimpson, Cheryl Wold. Illustrations: Reka Serfozo. Design: Winston Pei.

Henry and Eliza, by Jane Austen
1996. Edited by Karen L. Hartnick. Preface: Rachel M. Brownstein. Annotations: Catherine Gowl, Karen L. Hartnick, Maggie Hartnick, Ann Kelly, Cassie Marlantes. Afterword: Ann Kelly. Illustrations: Sarah Wagner-McCoy. Design: Winston Pei.

A Quiet Game, by Margaret Atwood
1997. Edited by Sherrill Grace and Kathy Chung. Introduction: Sherrill Grace. Annotations: Kathy Chung and Sherrill Grace. Illustrations: Kathy Chung. Design: Winston Pei.

The Young Visiters, by Daisy Ashford
1997. Edited by Juliet McMaster. Introduction: Jeffrey Mather. Textual Editing and Annotations: Celeste Bowering, Barbara Falk, Jeffrey Mather, Juliet McMaster, Monika Scharfenburger. Illustrations: Bruce Watson. Design: Winston Pei.

Editorial Teams

My Angria and the Angrians, by Charlotte Brontë
1997. Edited by Juliet McMaster, Leslie Robertson and the students of English 672. Introduction: Leslie Robertson. Textual editing: Astrid Blodgett, Carol-Ann Farkas, Jeffrey Herrle, Sherryl Maglione, and Leslie Robertson. Annotations: Carol-Ann Farkas, Jeffrey Herrle, Douglas Lewis, Erin McLaughlin, Juliet McMaster, Leslie Robertson, Barbara Simler, Robert Summers. "'The Best Book' and This Book": Douglas Lewis. Illustrations: Shannon Goetze. Design: Winston Pei.

Embryo Words, by Margaret Laurence.
1997. Edited by Nora Foster Stovel. Introduction: Nora Foster Stovel. Supplementary Information and Explanatory Notes: Lesley Belcourt, Anne Coté, Barbara Falk, Lisa Grekul, Jun Ling Khoo, Krissy Lundberg, Jennifer Prestash, Chris Riegel, Jodie Sinnema, Kim Solga and Nora Foster Stovel. Illustrations: Anne Coté and Jodie Sinnema. Design: Winston Pei, assisted by Jodie Sinnema.

A Collection of Letters, by Jane Austen.
1998. Edited by Juliet McMaster and the students of English 665. Introduction: Heather Harper. Textual Editing: Tobi Kozakewich, Kelly Laycock, Kirsten Macleod. Annotations: Christina Barabash, Heather Harper, Heather Kitteringham, Tobi Kozakewich, Kelly Laycock, Kirsten MacLeod, Juliet McMaster, Marcella Poirier and Jennifer Prestash. Illustrations: Laura Neilson. Design: Winston Pei, assisted by Laura Neilson.

Lesley Castle, by Jane Austen.
1998. Edited by Jan Fergus and the students of English 290 at Lehigh University: Anne Banas, Erin Harrison, Page Keith, Anna Pezik, Elibed Sanchez, Eli Stern, Ron Voloshin. Introduction: Jan Fergus. Illustrations: Juliet McMaster. Design: Winston Pei.

Satan in a Barrel, and other early stories, by Malcolm Lowry.
1999. Edited by Sherrill Grace. Introduction and Annotations: Sherrill Grace. Illustrations: Jason Collinge. Design: Winston Pei

Editorial Teams

Evelyn, by Jane Austen.
1999. Edited by Peter Sabor and the Eighteenth-Century Research Group at Université Laval, Québec. Introduction: Victoria Kortes-Papp. Textual editing: Victoria Kortes-Papp and Peter Sabor. Annotations: Sylvia Hunt, with Pamela Cheers, Graciela Moreira, Peter Sabor, and Anne Zylka. Map: Yan Kestens. Illustrations: Pauline Morel. Design: Winston Pei

Albion and Marina, by Charlotte Brontë.
1999. Edited by Juliet McMaster and the students of English 696. Introduction: Cindy Chopoidalo and Karen Clark. Textual editing: Jean Richardson, Juliet McMaster, Heather Meek, Jodie Sinnema. Annotation: Cindy Chopoidalo, Karen Clark, Karen Doerksen, Robyn Fowler, Juliet McMaster, Wendy Rabel, Jean Richardson. Appendix: Wendy Rabel. Illustrations: Shannon Goetze. Design: Winston Pei.

Colors of Speech, by Margaret Laurence.
2000. Edited by Nora Foster Stovel. Introduction: Nora Foster Stovel. Annotation: Lisa Grekul, Jun Ling Khoo, Krissy Lundberg, Marcella Poirier, Jennifer Prestash, Kim Solga, Nora Foster Stovel, Tracy Wright. Illustration: Jodie Sinnema. Design: Winston Pei.

The Adventurer, by Lady Mary Pierrepont.
2000. Edited by Isobel Grundy and the students of English 696. Introduction: Megan Crosland and Isobel Grundy. Textual editing: Isobel Grundy, Peni Christopher, Megan Crosland, Heather Harper, Susan Liepert, Stan Ruecker. Annotation: Isobel Grundy, Peni Christopher, Megan Crosland, Heather Harper, Susan Liepert. Illustrations: Susan Liepert. Design: Stan Ruecker.

Early Voices, by Greg Hollingshead, Carol Shields, Aritha van Herk, Rudy Wiebe.
2001. Edited by T. L. Walters and James King. Introduction: T. L. Walters. Textual editing: T. L. Walters and James King. Illustrations: Heidi Hudspith and Amanda Patey. Design: Winston Pei.

Editorial Teams

Jack & Alice, by Jane Austen.
2001. Edited by Joseph Wiesenfarth with Laura Maestrelli and Kristin Smith.
Illustrations: Juliet McMaster. Design: Winston Pei.

Peter Paul Rubens and Other Friendly Folk, by Opal Whiteley.
2001. Edited by Laura Cappello, Juliet McMaster, Lesley Peterson and Chris
Wangler. Illustrations: Juliet McMaster. Design: Winston Pei.

Tales of the Islanders, by Charlotte Brontë.
2001. Edited by Christine Alexander and the students of English 5032 at the
University of New South Wales. Introduction: Christine Alexander et al. Tex-
tual Editing and Appendix: Jessica Morath, Judy Diamond, Supakarn Iamharit,
Ai Hua Lim. Annotation: Elizabeth Connolly, Jacklyn Comer, Jonathan
Hindmarsh, Allyx Lathrope, Jessica Morath. Design: Winston Pei.

Sunbeams from a Golden Machine, by Marian Engel.
2002. Edited by Afra Kavanagh and Tammy MacNeil. Introduction and Annotations: Afra Kavanagh and Tammy MacNeil. Illustrations: Basma Kavanagh.
Design: Winston Pei.

Frederic & Elfrida, by Jane Austen.
2002. Edited by Peter Sabor with Sylvia Hunt and Victoria Kortes-Papp. Introduction: Sylvia Hunt. Textual Editing: Victoria Kortes-Papp and Peter Sabor.
Annotations: Peter Sabor. Illustrations: Juliet McMaster. Design: Winston Pei.